the mountaintop of marriage

A Vision Retreat Guidebook for Couples

Jimmy & Karen Evans

The Mountaintop of Marriage
ISBN 1-931585-24-5

2 3 4 5 6 7 8 9 10

Printed in the United States of America

MarriageToday™ | PO Box 59888 | Dallas, Texas 75229 | 972.953.0500 | marriagetoday.com

the power of vision

Come, and let us go up to the mountain of the lord...

He will teach us His ways and we shall walk in His paths...

Micah 4:2 NKJV

If you have been exposed to the ministry of MarriageToday for any time at all, you have probably heard my wife Karen and I share the story of how God healed and restored our marriage. You will also know that I went on to pastor a rapidly growing church where we counseled many other couples who were struggling in their marriages.

In my early years as a pastor, I read everything I could get my hands on concerning leadership and church growth. I remember one book in particular that had a big impact on my thinking. In it, I read that I needed to make sure I had a vision for my church. The author declared that if I didn't have a clear, well-articulated vision for the church, I might as well close the doors because nothing else I did was going to have much effect.

The book pointed to Proverbs 29:18 KJV which says, "Where there is no vision, the people perish." The word "perish" there means "unrestrained." I learned that you cannot keep two people or a group of people going the same direction for very long when there's not an established vision. You just end up wandering around and running in circles. Invariably, you get discouraged and quit because you realize, "I'm not getting anywhere."

So I determined that we were going to have a clear vision in our ministry. I told our staff, "We're going to pray until we get God's vision for this church." And God gave us a glorious one. We wrote it down and we kept it before us.

That vision kept us unified and moving forward. And we saw tremendous results. The power of vision to bring focus and growth was amazing.

It was several years, however, before the Lord was able to bring a troubling fact to my attention:

Though I had sought and received a compelling, God-given vision for the church I pastored, I hadn't really taken the time to develop a clear vision for my marriage or family!

The person God used to bring that omission home to me was my friend David Smith. At that time, David was the Associate Pastor of a large church in Edmond, Oklahoma. I had known David for many years and throughout that time I had always known him to be a walking advertisement for marriage and for his wife, Linda. They clearly had a great relationship and a thriving family.

One day when David and I were together, I heard him mention that he and Linda were getting ready to go on their annual "vision retreat." Of course, my response was, "What's a vision retreat?"

David went on to explain that years ago he and Linda had decided to take a few days away to allow God to speak to them about their marriage and to make sure they were on the same page regarding goals, priorities and values—in other words, "vision." He also described how they had made a practice of taking an annual "vision retreat" in which they spent time together allowing God to refine that vision.

That's when it hit me. I had never applied the powerful and biblical vision principle to the most important facet of my life—my home. Karen and I took immediate steps to correct that omission.

After many years of investing time in an annual vision retreat, Karen and I can tell you it is one of the most powerful and productive things you can do for your marriage and family. We learned a lot from David and Linda about how to have an effective retreat. And along the way we've learned some things ourselves.

The guide you now hold in your hands has incorporated that wisdom and experience—offering you a roadmap for conducting your own fulfilling vision retreat. Of course, not every question or topic will apply to your specific situation. Feel free to adopt what fits and adapt the rest.

your vision retreat
frequently asked questions

Q Do we have to go away to have a vision retreat? Can't we do this at home?

A While it is theoretically possible to gain the benefits of a vision retreat without leaving home, it is very difficult. The distractions of kids, phones and household tasks all work against the objectives of the retreat. A retreat, by definition, is a season of time away from the familiar and the busy-ness of everyday life.

Q Does a vision retreat have to be expensive?

A Not at all. You don't have to book a luxury resort in an exotic locale to have a powerful retreat (but if you can, more power to you!) A motel room on the other side of town or the guest room of a friend can be just as effective. The important thing is to get alone together and get quiet.

. . . .

Q How long should a vision retreat be?

A We have found that at least two or three days is ideal. While it is possible to do some good in a single day, and any amount of time is better than none at all, you really need at least two days and nights alone together to accomplish the steps we lay out in this guide.

>>>

Q Should we take our children?

A Please don't. Resist the temptation to feel guilty about making appropriate arrangements for them. The greatest thing you can do for your children is to have a strong marriage.

Q Do we have to spend the entire time locked in a room?

A No, on the contrary. This time should be fun, romantic, relaxing and invigorating. Recreation and entertainment are key parts of this time away.

Q What should we take on our retreat?

A Karen and I take our Bibles, notebooks, some worship music and, most importantly, a sense of anticipation that God is going to meet us there and do a work in our hearts.

preparation

Write the vision and make it plain on tablets,

that he may run who reads it.

Habakkuk 2:2 KJV

"A clearly understood vision that we write down keeps us motivated and focused. This is a powerful key of success in any endeavor of life."

Jimmy Evans

before the retreat

1 Several days or weeks before the date of your retreat, begin studying and praying over the questions in Part Two of this guide. Ask the Holy Spirit to illuminate and soften your heart where those questions are concerned.

2 Can you think of any other questions or issues that you should address as a couple that aren't covered in this guide? If so, add them to your journal.

3 Surrender your heart to the Lord and ask Him if there is anything you're doing wrong in your marriage for which you need to repent to your spouse. If so, be sure to do so at the very beginning of your time away together.

Consider including many or all of the following elements into your vision retreat. Work these activities into your planning, preparation and resources.

prayer
Pray with each other and for each other.

. . . .

Bible study
Use a devotional or go through a study together.

. . . .

journaling
Use this guide to journal your thoughts, inspirations and impressions as you spend time with God and with one another.

. . . .

fun
Do things together that you both enjoy.

>>>

romance

Be intentional and thoughtful about stoking the fire of passion in your relationship.

. . . .

communication

Talk! Even if it's not your nature or temperament to do so! Use the questions on the following pages to get things started.

. . . .

worship

You can bring along a music CD you both enjoy and make music a key part of your time with God. Worship has a way of opening the ears of our hearts to the voice of the Lord.

the retreat

When people do not accept divine guidance,
they run wild. But whoever obeys the law is happy.

Proverbs 29:18 NLT

"When two people are together in any endeavor in life, it is only possible for them to remain unified and productive if they both share the same vision and purpose. Therefore, it is of paramount importance that every couple hoping to succeed take the time and energy to get God's vision for their marriage."

Jimmy Evans

starting right

Begin your retreat together with a time of prayer and repentance. In a spirit of humility and transparency, lay out anything the Holy Spirit revealed to you during your preparation time. Invite the Holy Spirit's presence during your retreat and ask the Lord to impart vision, build unity and refresh your souls.

Note: Do not pressure your spouse to repent nor start the time with confrontation. This is not a time to point out to your spouse all of the things you think they need to change. Each of you should personally focus on the only person you have the power to change— you. Trust God to speak to your spouse.

Throughout the remainder of the retreat, you can use the questions on the following pages as discussion starters. As you come into agreement, write down your answers. You will find those answers very helpful when you begin to craft your marriage and family visions statements.

defining the broader vision for your marriage
What is our family vision and philosophy?

— purpose & principles —

Why did God put us together?

_____
_____
_____
_____

Individually and as a couple, what has God called us to accomplish in the coming year to further His purpose, and how can we work together to accomplish it?

as a couple: _____
_____
_____

as individuals: _____
_____
_____

What are the major ethical and moral standards that we want our family to live by?

_____
_____
_____
_____

What kinds of things would we want people to say in our eulogies when we're gone?

_____
_____
_____
_____

Are there any words of correction or direction God is speaking to us?

_____

_____

_____

_____

— family traditions & values —

What are our family's most deeply held values and beliefs?

_____

_____

_____

What are our giftings and passions as a family?

_____

_____

_____

What things (events, activities, commitments) tend to create the most stress in our household schedule? How can we lower that stress?

_____

_____

_____

_____

How would we like our family, relatives and guests to feel when they enter our home? What specific things can we do to create and maintain that atmosphere?

_____

_____

_____

_____

_____

What would our family look like if it really turned out well?

_____

_____

_____

— children & grandchildren —

How can we transmit our values to our children?

_____

_____

_____

What memories of family life would we like our children to hold dear? What specifically would we have to do, change, or eliminate from our lives now in order to produce those memories?

_____

_____

_____

What would we like to teach our children about spiritual development and our own personal beliefs?

_____

_____

_____

How can we discipline our children while still showing that we love them and protecting their self-esteem? How can we operate as a team in doing this? How can we be sure to avoid undermining one another in applying correction?

_____

_____

_____

_____

goals, plans & vision

With God's help, create a statement of vision and establish goals for each of the following areas of your lives. Use the calendar section which follows to log planned events, milestones and specific targets dates for reaching your goals.

— defining specific goals or vision —

Spirituality—individually, as a couple & as a family:

a. goals: _____

_____

_____

_____

b. plans/actions: _____

_____

_____

_____

c. vision: _____

_____

_____

_____

Service to God with our time, talents & treasure:

a. goals: _____

_____

_____

_____

_____

b. plans/actions: _____

_____

_____

_____

c. vision: _____

_____

_____

_____

Romance & sexual intimacy:

a. goals: _____

_____

_____

_____

b. plans/actions: _____

_____

_____

_____

c. vision: _____

_____

_____

_____

Finances:

a. goals: _____

_____

_____

_____

b. plans/actions: _____

_____

_____

_____

c. vision: _____

_____

_____

_____

Work/profession/career:

a. goals: _____

_____

_____

_____

b. plans/actions: _____

_____

_____

_____

c. vision: _____

_____

_____

_____

Personal & family time management/stress reduction:

a. goals: _____

_____

_____

_____

b. plans/actions: _____

_____

_____

_____

c. vision: _____

_____

_____

_____

In-laws & extended family relationships:

a. goals: _____

_____

_____

_____

b. plans/actions: _____

_____

_____

_____

c. vision: _____

_____

_____

_____

Friendships—individually & as a couple:

a. goals: _____

_____

_____

_____

b. plans/actions: _____

_____

_____

_____

c. vision: _____

_____

_____

_____

Health & fitness:

a. goals: _____

_____

_____

_____

b. plans/actions: _____

_____

_____

_____

c. vision: _____

_____

_____

_____

Home—housework & responsibility:

a. goals: _____

_____

_____

_____

b. plans/actions: _____

_____

_____

_____

c. vision: _____

_____

_____

_____

Children and/or grandchildren:

List each child. Ask and answer for each: What unique gifts or callings do we see in him/her? What can we do help him/her develop those gifts and walk in that calling? What is God speaking to us about this child?

1. name: _____

_____

_____

_____

2. name: _____

_____

_____

_____

3. name: _____

_____

_____

_____

4. name: _____

_____

_____

_____

5. name: _____

_____

_____

_____

Other:

a. goals: _____

_____

_____

b. plans/actions: _____

_____

_____

c. vision: _____

_____

_____

Other:

a. goals: _____
_____
_____

b. plans/actions: _____
_____
_____

c. vision: _____
_____
_____

Other:

a. goals: _____
_____
_____

b. plans/actions: _____
_____
_____

c. vision: _____
_____
_____

12-month vision calendar

Use the following pages to establish specific targets for reaching goals as well as dates for special family milestones or happenings—then protect those dates!

month 1

date:_____ date:_____

event/milestone:_____ event/milestone:_____

_____ _____

_____ _____

_____ _____

date:_____ date:_____

event/milestone:_____ event/milestone:_____

_____ _____

_____ _____

_____ _____

goals to achieve this month:_____

_____

_____

_____

_____

_____

_____

notes:_____

_____

_____

_____

_____

_____

_____

month 2

date:_____
event/milestone:_____
_____
_____
_____

date:_____
event/milestone:_____
_____
_____
_____

date:_____
event/milestone:_____
_____
_____
_____

date:_____
event/milestone:_____
_____
_____
_____

goals to achieve this month:_____
_____
_____
_____
_____
_____

notes:_____
_____
_____
_____
_____
_____
_____

month 3

date:_____   date:_____

event/milestone:_____   event/milestone:_____

_____   _____

_____   _____

_____   _____

date:_____   date:_____

event/milestone:_____   event/milestone:_____

_____   _____

_____   _____

_____   _____

goals to achieve this month:_____

_____

_____

_____

_____

_____

_____

notes:_____

_____

_____

_____

_____

_____

_____

month 4

date:_____   date:_____
event/milestone:_____   event/milestone:_____
_____   _____
_____   _____
_____   _____

date:_____   date:_____
event/milestone:_____   event/milestone:_____
_____   _____
_____   _____
_____   _____

goals to achieve this month:_____
_____
_____
_____
_____
_____
_____

notes:_____
_____
_____
_____
_____
_____
_____

month 5

date:_____   date:_____
event/milestone:_____   event/milestone:_____
_____   _____
_____   _____
_____   _____

date:_____   date:_____
event/milestone:_____   event/milestone:_____
_____   _____
_____   _____
_____   _____

goals to achieve this month:_____
_____
_____
_____
_____
_____
_____

notes:_____
_____
_____
_____
_____
_____
_____

month 6

date:_____   date:_____

event/milestone:_____   event/milestone:_____

_____   _____

_____   _____

_____   _____

date:_____   date:_____

event/milestone:_____   event/milestone:_____

_____   _____

_____   _____

_____   _____

goals to achieve this month:_____

_____

_____

_____

_____

_____

_____

notes:_____

_____

_____

_____

_____

_____

_____

month 7

date:_____   date:_____
event/milestone:_____   event/milestone:_____
_____   _____
_____   _____
_____   _____

date:_____   date:_____
event/milestone:_____   event/milestone:_____
_____   _____
_____   _____
_____   _____

goals to achieve this month:_____
_____
_____
_____
_____
_____
_____

notes:_____
_____
_____
_____
_____
_____

month 8

date:_____   date:_____
event/milestone:_____   event/milestone:_____
_____   _____
_____   _____
_____   _____

date:_____   date:_____
event/milestone:_____   event/milestone:_____
_____   _____
_____   _____
_____   _____

goals to achieve this month:_____
_____
_____
_____
_____
_____
_____

notes:_____
_____
_____
_____
_____
_____
_____

month 9

date:_____   date:_____
event/milestone:_____   event/milestone:_____
_____   _____
_____   _____
_____   _____

date:_____   date:_____
event/milestone:_____   event/milestone:_____
_____   _____
_____   _____
_____   _____

goals to achieve this month:_____
_____
_____
_____
_____
_____

notes:_____
_____
_____
_____
_____
_____

month 10

date:_____   date:_____

event/milestone:_____   event/milestone:_____

_____   _____

_____   _____

_____   _____

date:_____   date:_____

event/milestone:_____   event/milestone:_____

_____   _____

_____   _____

_____   _____

goals to achieve this month:_____

_____

_____

_____

_____

_____

_____

notes:_____

_____

_____

_____

_____

_____

_____

month 11

date:_____   date:_____
event/milestone:_____   event/milestone:_____
_____   _____
_____   _____
_____   _____

date:_____   date:_____
event/milestone:_____   event/milestone:_____
_____   _____
_____   _____
_____   _____

goals to achieve this month:_____
_____
_____
_____
_____
_____
_____

notes:_____
_____
_____
_____
_____
_____
_____

month 12

date:_____

event/milestone:_____

_____

_____

_____

date:_____

event/milestone:_____

_____

_____

_____

date:_____

event/milestone:_____

_____

_____

_____

date:_____

event/milestone:_____

_____

_____

_____

goals to achieve this month:_____

_____

_____

_____

_____

_____

_____

notes:_____

_____

_____

_____

_____

_____

_____

3

finishing and following through

"For I know the plans that I have for you," declares the LORD, "plans for welfare and not for calamity to give you a future and a hope."

Jeramiah 29:11 NAS

"God is a good God. When you are seeing His vision for your life, marriage and family—it will always excite you and promise to fulfill the desires of your heart."

Jimmy Evans

developing an overall marriage & family vision statement

As a final phase of your retreat, you are now ready to take everything you have learned and recorded above, along with everything God has spoken to you, and use it to build an overall vision statement for your family. As you do:

1 Pray and ask God to lead and guide you as you develop your Family Vision Statement.

2 Look at your answers to the questions above and identify key words that you want to use in your vision statement.

3 Try to keep the statement short and simple.

4 Develop a motto that will describe your vision statement.

5 Find a Scripture that represents your vision statement.

After you have developed your vision statement, evaluate your statement by asking the following questions:

1. In one or two words, how would you characterize the focus of your vision statement and does it reflect what you want your family to be?

2. Does it incorporate the important areas of life: the spiritual, relational, personal, family/parental and financial?

3. Does it represent each spouse's most cherished beliefs? Is it properly balanced to reflect your individual perspectives?

the summary of our vision

date:_____

following through

As you close your time together, commit to yourselves and to the Lord to revisit this journal as you keep your vision and goals before you. Track your progress and your victories. And make plans now to do this again next year.

journal

_____
_____
_____
_____
_____
_____
_____
_____
_____
_____
_____
_____
_____
_____
_____
_____
_____
_____
_____
_____
_____
_____
_____
_____
_____
_____
_____

about Jimmy and Karen Evans

"Your family has a great future!" That's the message of hope Jimmy and Karen Evans have been proclaiming for more than twenty years. It's a message close to their hearts, for it is one born out of personal experience...

Their Story of Restoration

Harsh words had been spoken. Angry accusations had been made. The edict "pack your bags and get out of this house and my life!" had been issued to a sobbing Karen.

That's when the Evans found themselves standing in a place they never expected to be... on the brink of divorce.

Devastated, Jimmy breathed a prayer asking for God's help. Immediately, the Holy Spirit swept in bringing both conviction for sin, and an outpouring of the limitless mercy of God.

That night a verse of scripture rang true in Jimmy's heart (John 14:26). He realized the Father had sent the Holy Spirit to teach him "all things" which meant, the Holy Spirit could teach him how to become the husband God intended for him to be.

That's when a journey of discovery in God's Word began for the Evans. The foundation of their marriage was shored up as they applied the biblical principles they learned. Jimmy and Karen's relationship began to grow and flourish. Their marriage became Rock Solid.

And that's when Jimmy and Karen Evans once again found themselves standing in a place they never expected to be... a place of heaven on earth!

Now, with a deep love for one another and a joy they didn't know was possible, Jimmy and Karen say with all confidence, "Your family has a great future!"

God did it for them, and they know He can and will do it for you!

You'll find additional resources for strengthening and enriching

your marriage at MarriageToday's website:

www.MarriageToday.com

Come, and let us go up to the mountain

of the lord... He will teach us His ways

and we shall walk in His paths...

Micah 4:2 NKJV